GLAD DAY

GLAD DAY

and other
classical poems
for
children

chosen and illustrated
by

Ronald Himler

G. P. Putnam's Sons
New York

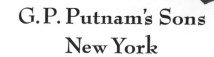

ACKNOWLEDGMENTS

Grateful acknowledgment is made to the following for permission to reprint these poems: to The Bodley Head for permission to reprint the poem "Kitty: What She Thinks of Herself" by W. B. Rands; to Macmillan & Company Limited, London and Basingstoke, and The Macmillan Company of Canada Limited, and the Trustees of the Hardy Estate for permission to reprint "Weathers" by Thomas Hardy from *Collected Poems of Thomas Hardy*; to The Literary Trustees of Walter de la Mare, and The Society of Authors as their representative, for permission to reprint "Bunches of Grapes" by Walter de la Mare from *The Complete Poems of Walter de la Mare*; and to Mr. Kerrison Preston of The Georgian House, Merstham, Surrey, for permission to reprint the first and last verses of "Glad Day" by W. Graham Robertson and to use its title as the title of this book.

Library of Congress Catalog Card Number: 72-160336
PRINTED IN THE UNITED STATES OF AMERICA
All Ages

for
Danny

THE POEMS

GLAD DAY

Here's another day, dear,
　　Here's the sun again
Peeping in his pleasant way
　　Through the window pane.
　　Rise and let him in, dear,
　　Hail him "hip hurray!"
Now the fun will all begin.
　　Here's another day!

Such a lot to do, dear,

Such a lot to see!

How we ever can get through

Fairly puzzles me.

Hurry up and out, dear,

Then—away! away!

In and out and round about,

Here's another day!

W. Graham Robertson

ALL BUSY

The cock's on the house-top,
    Blowing his horn;
The bull's in the barn,
    A-threshing of corn;
The maids in the meadows
    Are making the hay,
The ducks in the river
    are swimming away.

THE COW

Thank you, pretty cow, that made
Pleasant milk to soak my bread,
Every day, and every night,
Warm, and fresh, and sweet, and white.

Do not chew the hemlock rank,
Growing on the weedy bank;
But the yellow cowslips eat,
They will make it very sweet.

Where the purple violet grows,
Where the bubbling water flows,
Where the grass is fresh and fine,
Pretty cow, go there and dine.

Ann and Jane Taylor

CURLY LOCKS

Curly locks! Curly locks!

Wilt thou be mine?

Thou shalt not wash dishes

Nor yet feed the swine.

But sit on a cushion

And sew a fine seam,

And feed upon strawberries

Sugar and cream.

MY MAID MARY

My maid Mary she minds the dairy,

    While I go a-hoeing and a-mowing each morn;

Gaily run the reel and the little spinning-wheel,

    Whilst I am singing and mowing my corn.

WHAT THE BIRDS SAY

Do you know what the birds say? The sparrow, the dove,

The linnet and thrush say "I love and I love!"

In the winter they're silent — the wind is so strong;

What it says I don't know, but it sings a loud song.

But green leaves, and blossoms, and sunny warm weather,

And singing, and loving, all come back together.

And the lark is so brimful of gladness and love,

The green fields below him, the blue sky above,

That he sings, and he sings, and for ever sings he —

"I love my love, and my love loves me!"

Samuel Taylor Coleridge

THREE THINGS TO REMEMBER

A Robin Redbreast in a cage
Puts all Heaven in a rage.

A skylark wounded on the wing
Doth make a cherub cease to sing.

He who shall hurt the little wren
Shall never be beloved by men.

William Blake

BUNCHES OF GRAPES

'Bunches of grapes,' says Timothy;
'Pomegranates pink,' says Elaine;
'A junket of cream and a cranberry tart
　　For me,' says Jane.

'Love-in-a-mist,' says Timothy;
'Primroses pale,' says Elaine;
'A Nosegay of pinks and mignonette
　　For me,' says Jane.

'Chariots of gold,' says Timothy;
'Silvery wings,' says Elaine;
'A bumpity ride in a waggon of hay
　　For me,' says Jane.

Walter de la Mare

MERRY ARE THE BELLS

Merry are the bells, and merry would they ring,
Merry was myself, and merry could I sing;
With a merry ding-dong, happy, gay, and free,
And a merry sing-song, happy let us be!

Waddle goes your gait, and hollow are your hose;
Noddle goes your pate, and purple is your nose;
Merry is your sing-song, happy, gay, and free;
With a merry ding-dong, happy let us be!

Merry have we met, and merry have we been;
Merry let us part, and merry meet again;
With our merry sing-song, happy, gay, and free,
With a merry ding-dong, happy let us be!

I SAW A SHIP A-SAILING

I saw a ship a-sailing,
    A-sailing on the sea;
And it was full of pretty things
    For baby and for me.

    There were sweetmeats in the cabin,
        And apples in the hold;
    The sails were made of silk,
        And the masts were made of gold.

        The four-and-twenty sailors
           That stood between the decks,
      Were four-and-twenty white mice,
          With chains about their necks.

          The captain was a duck,
             With packet on his back;
         And when the ship began to move,
            The captain cried, "Quack, quack!"

FERRY ME ACROSS THE WATER

"Ferry me across the water,
   Do, boatman, do."
"If you've a penny in your purse
   I'll ferry you."

"I have a penny in my purse,
   And my eyes are blue;
So ferry me across the water,
   Do, boatman, do."

"Step into my ferry-boat,
   Be they black or blue,
And for the penny in your purse
   I'll ferry you."

Christina Rossetti

WEATHERS

I

This is the weather the cuckoo likes,
    And so do I;
When showers betumble the chestnut spikes,
    And nestlings fly;
And the little brown nightingale bills his best,
    And they sit outside at "The Travellers' Rest,"
And maids come forth sprig-muslin drest,
And citizens dream of the south and west,
    And so do I.

II

This is the weather the shepherd shuns,
    And so do I;
When beeches drip in browns and duns,
    And thresh, and ply;
And hill-hid tides throb, throe on throe,
And meadow rivulets overflow,
And drops on gate-bars hang in a row,
And rooks in families homeward go,
    And so do I.

Thomas Hardy

WHO HAS SEEN THE WIND?

Who has seen the wind?
  Neither I nor you:
But when the leaves hang trembling,
  The wind is passing through.

Who has seen the wind?
  Neither you nor I:
But when the trees bow down their heads,
  The wind is passing by.

Christina Rossetti

POOR ROBIN

The north wind doth blow,

And we shall have snow,

And what will poor Robin do then, poor thing?

He'll sit in the barn,

And keep himself warm,

And hide his head under his wing, poor thing!

KITTY: WHAT SHE THINKS OF HERSELF

I am the Cat of Cats. I am

    The everlasting cat!

Cunning, and old, and sleek as jam,

    The everlasting cat!

I hunt the vermin in the night —

    The everlasting cat!

For I see best without the light —

    The everlasting cat!

W. B. Rands

SAFE IN BED

Matthew, Mark, Luke and John,

Bless the bed that I lie on!

Four corners to my bed,

Five angels there lie spread;

Two at my head,

Two at my feet,

One at my heart, my soul to keep.

THE MOON

O, look at the moon !

    She is shining up there ;

O mother, she looks

    Like a lamp in the air.

Last week she was smaller,

    And shaped like a bow ;

But now she's grown bigger,

    And round as an O.

Eliza Lee Follen

DREAMS TO SELL

If there were dreams to sell,

    What would you buy?

Some cost a passing bell;

    Some a light sigh,

That shakes from Life's fresh crown

Only a rose-leaf down.

If there were dreams to sell,

Merry and sad to tell,

And the crier rang the bell,

    What would you buy?

T. L. Beddoes

THE HAPPY PIPER

Piping down the valleys wild,
   Piping songs of pleasant glee,
On a cloud I saw a child,
   And he laughing said to me:

   "Pipe a song about a Lamb!"
      So I piped with merry cheer.
   "Piper, pipe that song again";
      So I piped: he wept to hear.

"Drop thy pipe, thy happy pipe;

Sing thy songs of happy cheer!"

So I sang the same again,

While he wept with joy to hear.

"Piper, sit thee down and write

In a book that all may read."

So he vanish'd from my sight,

And I pluck'd a hollow reed,

And I made a rural pen,

And I stain'd the water clear,

And I wrote my happy songs

Every child may joy to hear.

William Blake

THE ARTIST

An eminently talented newcomer to children's book illustrating, RONALD HIMLER was born in Cleveland and studied at the Cleveland Institute of Art, the Cranbrook Academy of Art in Michigan, and New York University. He worked for a time as a counselor at the Hartford Regional Center for Retarded Children in Connecticut and as an industrial sculptor. Mr. Himmler has traveled extensively in Europe and now makes his home in New York City. GLAD DAY is his first book for Putnam's.